I am Miss

by Kaye Umansky

THE CAST

BEN

MOUSE

JOJO

SAM

MRS TURNER
(The head teacher)

MISS CHERRY
(The class teacher)

Scene 1

The Staff Room. Mrs Turner is drinking tea. There is a knock at the door.

Enter Ben, Mouse and Jojo, with bags and boxes full of jumble.

BEN   We have some things for the jumble sale, Mrs Turner.

MRS TURNER   Oh, good. Put them all over there please, Ben.

MOUSE   My bag is torn. The toys are falling out.

MRS TURNER   Oh dear. Can you pick them up?

A telephone rings.

3

MRS TURNER   My telephone is ringing.

She exits.

JOJO   What a mess.

MOUSE   The bag was torn.

BEN   We will help you, Mouse.

They pick up the toys.

BEN   Here is your old rabbit, Jojo.

MOUSE   And my red car.

JOJO   And Pip's old rattle.

MOUSE   That used to be mine.

He shakes the rattle.

JOJO   Sssh! We are here to do a job, not play about.

5

Scene 2

The classroom. Miss Cherry is giving a big bag of clothes to Sam.

MISS CHERRY Here are some old clothes for the jumble sale.

SAM Are they yours?

MISS CHERRY Yes. Will you take them to the Staff Room for me please, Sam?

SAM Yes, Miss Cherry.

MISS CHERRY Thank you. Come right back.

SAM I will.

Exit Sam with the bag.

wish

bush

shop

DINOSAURS

DINOSAURS

7

Scene 3

The Staff Room. Ben, Mouse and Jojo have just finished picking up the toys. There is a knock at the door.

Enter Sam.

SAM	Hello, you lot.
JOJO	Is that more jumble?
SAM	Yes. Miss Cherry gave it to me.
BEN	Mrs Turner wants it over there.

He points to the corner.

SAM	So this is where the teachers live.
BEN	They don't live here, Sam.
MOUSE	They go home at night.

9

Sam puts the bag down.
A jumper falls out.

SAM   Oh, look. Here is Miss Cherry's nice red jumper.

JOJO   Put it back.

SAM   I want to try it on.

BEN   No, Sam, no!

Sam puts on the jumper.

SAM   How do I look?

MOUSE   Sam! Take it off!

SAM   Here is her hat. I like this hat.

Sam puts on the hat.

BEN	Stop it, Sam!
SAM	Oh look! Her shoes!
JOJO	No! No!

Sam puts on the shoes.

SAM	Now I am Miss Cherry. You must do as I say.
BEN	Sam! Stop it.
SAM	Sit down please, everyone.
MOUSE	You are being bad, Sam.
SAM	Did you hear me, Mouse Macdonald? Please sit down.

Ben, Jojo and Mouse sit down, giggling.

SAM	We will start with sums. Mouse Macdonald. What is two add two?
MOUSE	Six, Miss Cherry.
SAM	Silly boy. Do you know, Jojo Macdonald?
JOJO	Four, Miss Cherry.
	The door opens. Mrs Turner and Miss Cherry peep around. Sam does not see them. Ben does.
SAM	Good girl. Now, take out your books. It's time to read.
BEN	Sam!
SAM	I am not Sam. I am Miss Cherry.

MISS CHERRY Who am I, then?

Sam turns and sees them. They are laughing.

SAM Oh dear.

MOUSE Please don't be cross with her.

MISS CHERRY We are not cross, are we, Mrs Turner?

MRS TURNER No. We think you make a very good teacher, Sam.

MISS CHERRY But you do look funny in my hat!

The End